D1206118

SINGLE IS YOUR SUPER POWER

SINGLE IS YOUR SUPERPOWER

1. FIND YOUR SOUL
2. FIND YOUR SOULMATE

By: Case Kenny

New Mindset, Who Dis?™

Also by Case Kenny

New Mindset, Who Dis Podcast

This is my twice weekly podcast where I offer practical thoughts on self improvement, mindfulness and how to live your best life.

It's a different kind of podcast.

I'm just a dude living my life sharing my perspective.

No gurus, no fluff and no preaching of generic life advice... just my thoughts on self-help, wellness, and mindsets with practical and personal insights on how to live a passionate, purposeful, and happy life.

Join me on Mondays and Thursdays.

Check out newmindsetwhodis.com for more ways to discover your best self.

Chicago, IL

For you (you're a catch)

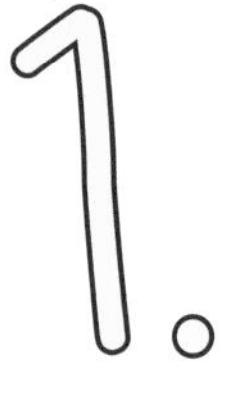

Nice to meet you

What to expect & how to make the most of this workbook.

Wanted cuddles, but got struggles?

Your past is powerful.

But why?

Know your WHY or keep going in circles.

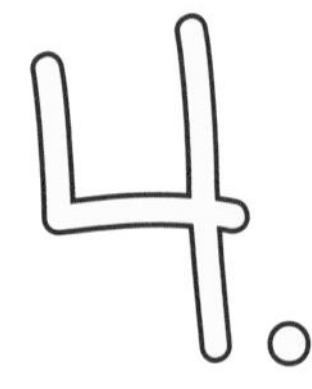

Stop being so thirsty

The "today" version of someone vs. the "tomorrow" version.

Put it down, flip it and reverse it

What are you looking for?

Kanye attitude, Drake feelings

Keep it simple.

Your "ho" phase

How to date (literally).

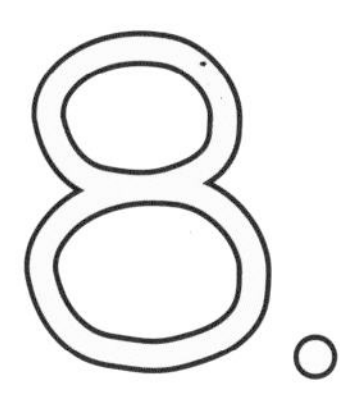

Looking is for free

Red flags, red flags, red flags.

Situationships

If you're unsure, stay single.

The real love language

Radical honesty.

You're more than just a snack

You were not designed to be liked by everyone.

Single is your Superpower

Open eyes, eager heart.

Chapter 1

NICE TO MEET YOU

Hello, my beautiful, talented, compassionate, and driven friend.

Yep, that's you.

In this short workbook, I hope to inspire you to shout that truth from a mountain.

And in doing so, I'm confident you're going to completely change how you date, what you look for in a partner, and how happy and content you are as you do.

After completing this workbook, I'm confident you're not going to hate dating anymore.

You're not going to be frustrated, discouraged, or convinced you'll never find your someone. Quite the opposite. You're going to enjoy dating! You're going to feel empowered, decisive, and at peace with yourself as you do!

So, let's get some quick intros out of the way.

You and me.

You...

"A beautiful, talented, compassionate, and driven human, who happens to be single right now."

You might be frustrated and "sooooo over" dating and relationships right now. You might have just gotten out of a serious relationship. You might currently be stuck in a cycle of jumping from one short, unfulfilling relationship to another. Or you might be taking a break from dating completely.

Regardless, you have a desire to get it right. You want to date intentionally, respect yourself, know what you deserve, and ultimately find "your person."

You're open, vulnerable, and eager to take a step back and find your sense of self during this single time, so you no longer waste your valuable energy on people who are not right for you.

And then there's me.

My name is Case Kenny. I'm a 32-year-old dude living and dating in Chicago.

I've been fortunate to have success as a podcaster on my podcast, New Mindset, Who Dis, and as a writer on all things mindfulness.

I am not a dating or relationship expert. You won't find me putting on relationship seminars over the weekend. I don't have a magical dating crystal ball that tells me the secret to your relationship woes.

But what I do have is perspective. I have perspective which has totally changed how I date, what I look for in a partner, and most importantly, what I see in myself.

I believe this is powerful perspective, because it has totally transformed my dating life. I now have the utmost confidence in myself, I know who I am and what I deserve, and I have the patience to see it through until I find "my person."

That is a far cry from how I used to be - miserably going through the paces of dating just to date.

I used to overthink every minute detail of dating.

I was shaken by rejection, mixed signals or disinterest. I didn't know what I wanted, ignored every single red flag and frankly was just fed up and ready to give up. I felt stuck in a cycle of meaningless dates, short relationships, chronic overthinking and confusing mixed emotions about what I was doing.

Fast forward to today and everything has changed. It's like I had a light bulb moment and never looked back.

I am confident, fulfilled and centered as I date. I know what I want, I make better decisions and I simply enjoy the process.

Why? Because I took time to make sense of what I wanted and how to get it.

Simply put, I found my sense of self and purpose in dating, and I want to help you find yours.

I want to help you enjoy your dating life. I want to help you be patient and enjoy the journey.

As you read my thoughts and complete the exercises in this workbook, you'll notice I say the word "we" quite a bit. I am not a professor. I am not lecturing to you. I am not telling you what to do. I am simply expressing to you what we can all do to make our dating lives more fulfilling.

We're in this together. There are no right or wrong answers - only personal decisions to do better.

It can be tough to know what's best for you, but now is a great time to push yourself to find clarity. Being single is a great opportunity to draw a line in the sand in regard to who you are and what you want.

That is why I say that...

single is your superpower.

While I can't tell you what decisions to make, I can give you some things to think about. And if there's anything I've learned over the past decade of dating, it's that the questions you ask yourself are the most important ingredient to finally getting it right.

When you ask yourself the right questions and you consider the right perspectives, you make better dating decisions. Plain and simple.

At the end of the day, all you can ask of yourself is to make better decisions.

All you can ask is to trust yourself, react quicker, and be brutally honest with yourself and others.

Dating is always going to be somewhat complicated. Relationships are never going to be easy. But you can control the decisions you make as you go about finding your person.

If you arm yourself with insight into who you are and what you deserve, and you have the confidence to never lose sight of that, you're going to be much happier and more patient as you date.

So, that's what I have to offer you.

Perspective, questions, and guidance.

I promise to keep it real with you. Everything I've written here comes directly from my experience living and dating in Chicago. No fluff, no lofty irrelevant advice, no advice lifted from today's hottest guru.

This is just me reflecting on how I've found my sense of self, my purpose, and my confidence in dating. This is me distilling 10 years of dating perspective into a short workbook, so you can arm yourself with perspective that has the power to transform how you date.

I mean it when I say *single is your superpower.*

Simply put, I designed this workbook to help you find your soul, so you can find your soulmate.

You do that when you're single!

This is a workbook to make the most of your single time. Completing this workbook will lead you to reclaim your sense of worth again. And in doing so, it will help you make better dating decisions and be happier and more purposeful as you do.

This isn't something you sit back, read, and come out thinking, "That was interesting."

Nah, this is perspective combined with action! Read each chapter and take action by answering the prompts. Consider the perspective and find your own clarity by putting pen to paper.

The workbook consists of 12 chapters of perspective, interwoven with exercises that lead you to connect with yourself, who you are, and finally understand who is right for you.

Read the words, consider the perspectives, complete the exercises, and I'm confident it will leave you with a sense of calm and resolve that will give you purpose in your dating life.

It will leave you knowing what you deserve, the red flags to avoid, and with the confidence to never settle.

Let's go.

What do you want in your dating life? (select as many as you want)

- [ ] I want to have more patience
- [ ] I want to no longer feel like I'm falling behind
- [ ] I want to stop dating the wrong people
- [ ] I want to feel less pressure to get it right
- [ ] I want to love myself more
- [ ] I want to stop giving my energy to the wrong people
- [ ] I want to find someone who deserves me
- [ ] I want to respect myself
- [ ] I want to know what I actually want in a partner
- [ ] I want to have the confidence to trust my intuition
- [ ] I want to stop overthinking
- [ ] I want to enjoy dating!

I am single right now because...

I am a catch because...

Chapter 2

WANTED CUDDLES BUT GOT STRUGGLES?

If you're reading this, you're single (or you're considering becoming single).

You might actively be dating, but you haven't found anything serious. You might be dating and have no idea what you're doing. You might not be dating at all.

Regardless, you're single in the sense that you have not yet found "your person."

You might have been through a lot getting to this point. You might have bought this workbook out of desperation or in a last-ditch attempt to finally get it right.

You might be beyond frustrated and "totally over dating."

And so, you might be having thoughts like:

All my friends have found their person. All I have are stories. All I have are lessons learned. I have nothing to show for myself.

Well, my friend, I want to get this workbook started off on the right foot, and that starts with you approaching the perspective and exercises on the following pages with the right view of yourself first.

I want you to wipe the slate clean. I need you to wipe the slate clean.

I know this is easier said than done but so important <3

Because I have news for you. How you view yourself is everything! The stories you tell yourself are everything!

I don't know you, but I do know you have something incredibly valuable that you might not realize.

While you have not found your person yet, and you might feel like you're falling behind, what you do have is something much more valuable.

You have a resolve to never settle.

That resolve is more powerful than being able to select "in a relationship" on Facebook, finally getting your parents off your back about dating, or having a plus-one to take to a wedding.

To know that you haven't settled - and have no intention of ever settling is something that so many people don't have...

I don't have any numbers to back this up, but I'm willing to bet there are a lot of people in relationships right now who, behind closed doors, while staring up at the ceiling at night, admit to themselves that they are settling.

They are settling for someone who is not their person. BUT their desire to not start over, to be comfortable, and to not fall behind relative to friends who are in committed relationships, trumps that realization.

And so, they just live in that settled world.

But you? You, my beautiful and driven friend! You say you have nothing to show?

You say you only have stories but no love?

You say all you have to show for yourself are...

- times you've been ghosted.

- times you've been "left on read."

- times you shared your deepest feelings, only to have them thrown in your face.

- times you finally thought you found your person, only to realize how wrong that person truly was for you.

I say you have something more valuable than love right now. You have something that so many "settlers" wish they could have but are too afraid to hit reset to get.

You have a determination to never settle.

You have the promise of hope.

You have something you hold on to.

Most of all, you have a sense of pride, knowing that even though you feel like you've been beaten up, or like you've run a marathon, you still refuse to lay down and call it quits. You still refuse to settle.

That is a really big deal!

Because love will come. It will! And it's my mission to show you how to enjoy your life while you work toward finding it.

Your resolve and stubbornness to never settle is something you should be proud of.

You have the gift of self-respect! You have the gift of self-love. You have the gift of knowing that you deserve more.

You have open eyes and an eager heart! That is a powerful combination. :)

That's a gift not everyone gets, because they've either settled and never looked back, or they've never dove deep to understand themselves in the first place.

But you, my friend, have been through a lot, and you're not afraid to wait a bit longer.

You refuse to not be appreciated. You refuse to be a second option.

You refuse to settle.

That is a promise you have made yourself, whether you realize it or not.

There are so many times where you could have settled, but you didn't, because you would rather appear to be falling behind than to live a lifetime knowing you didn't keep going.

You've opted for the tougher decision, but it's one that ultimately makes you whole, and I'm proud of you for that.

So please don't think you have nothing to show for yourself.

You have yourself to show.

Look at you! You're glowing! You're glowing with resolve and self-respect, and at the end of the day, THAT is what matters!

You have those stories and lessons as proof that you refuse to settle.

You have yourself to show, and that is something to be proud of.

Are we on the same page?

I need you to feel yourself right now. I need you to smile because of this realization.

I need you to have a foundation of pride going into this workboook.

I need you to know that I see this in you.

You haven't settled and you will never settle. That is something to be proud of.

That is your story!

To be happy and effective in your dating life, you have to take responsibility for the stories you tell yourself.

Then and only then will you open yourself up to have the right relationship, with the right person, based on the right values.

The stories you tell yourself about your dating life...

If you're single and you find yourself consistently disappointed, frustrated or saying things like, "All men are the same," or "Women are all crazy!" or "I'm probably just going to be disappointed, hurt, confused, cheated on," this will be particularly powerful for you.

Think about your dating life for a moment.

What are the patterns you see?

Consistently ghosted?

Consistently flirted with but nothing more?

Only finding a lack of communication or no follow-through?

Only finding people who "aren't looking for anything serious?"

Think about those patterns for a moment. Seriously think about them.

What are the patterns in your dating life that are consistently presenting themselves to you? What are the patterns that frustrate you? What makes you throw your hands up and swear off dating in favor of being that fun aunt/uncle who's always tipsy and traveling the world?

Ok, now ask yourself:

What are the stories you're telling yourself? Are they the same as those frustrations?

Have you created stories in your head that look something like this?

I'm single because...

"All men want is sex."

"Everyone cheats."

"No one understands or appreciates me."

"No one can handle me!"

"No one wants anything serious."

"No one is honest or has follow through."

Are those the types of stories you're telling yourself?

It's time to get real and take responsibility for those stories. It's time to step into your worth by setting new boundaries for yourself.

I seriously believe that the stories you tell yourself are the ones you'll end up living.

Call that a cheesy thing to say or label me an overly sensitive dude, but I've found (and I fundamentally believe) that the stories you tell yourself give the universe a sign to continue dishing-up heaps more of the same for you.

You're telling the universe what you want to order, so why are you surprised when it serves you up a nice plate of bullsh*t?

I'm not surprised that happens, when those are the stories you're telling yourself.

But here's the truth: those stories are not reflective of your worth. Those stories are not reflective of YOUR STORY!

You know that you deserve more than those things.

High standards, my friend!

Why are you telling the universe stories about what you don't deserve?

Those stories are telling the universe what to bring your way!

If you keep telling yourself that everyone cheats, you'll keep finding people who cheat.

If you keep telling yourself that you're only going to get hurt, you'll find someone who will hurt you.

If you keep telling yourself that everyone disappoints you, you'll find someone who will do just that.

But, my friend, remember that you can tell yourself any story you want.

You can observe, learn, and recognize that yes, some people suck. Yes, some men are pigs and some women are crazy. Some people are dishonest, and some will f**k you over. I'm not disputing that, and I'm sorry you've been through those experiences.

But those stories have nothing to do with your worth.

Know your worth by drawing a strong boundary that says you will not tolerate those things or people.

Tell yourself that! Tell yourself your worth!

Tell yourself your worth instead of those stories. Take responsibility for what you tell yourself.

Do you tolerate f***boys? No! Then stop saying that all men are f***boys!

Do you tolerate dishonesty? No! Then stop saying everyone is dishonest!

Do you tolerate playing games? No! Then stop saying everyone is playing games!

Tell yourself a different story and watch the universe serve THAT up.

Instead of crippling yourself by saying that what's happened in your dating life is the story of your life and it's all you'll ever get, flip the script and tell yourself stories about your worth and what you deserve.

Tell a story that says:

There are good people in this world.

There are people who communicate, are driven, honest and are ready to commit and build together.

There are kind, compassionate, driven people who want what's best for me.

Tell yourself THAT story!

When you take responsibility for the stories you tell yourself, you point yourself in the direction of people who respect your worth.

I really believe this!

The universe is listening, my friends! It's more in tune with you and the stories you tell yourself than you think.

Honor yourself by drawing a boundary and changing the stories you tell yourself!

Tell the universe what you want, instead of what you don't.

Tell the universe what you deserve, instead of what disappoints you.

Tell the universe the boundaries you've set, instead of the ways people have broken them in the past.

Tell the universe what you want, repeat stories that affirm your worth, and draw a boundary everywhere else. When you do that, I really believe the universe is listening and will serve you up more of what you deserve.

Now don't worry, I'm going to help you come up with those stories in this workbook. I'm going to help you find clarity on what you want and what you deserve, but I want you to consider this for a moment:

Consider the stories you've been telling yourself. Consider your frustrations. Consider all your failed relationships.

They are not just Ls. They're Ws. They are a reflection of you knowing that you deserve more, and you deserve better.

That is a powerful resolve to have! You have powerful stories to tell the universe!

You have open eyes and an eager heart.

That is your superpower.

Check all the things that have happened in your dating life.

- [ ] I've been ghosted
- [ ] I've ghosted someone
- [ ] I've been left on read
- [ ] I've been cheated on
- [ ] I've cheated on someoone
- [ ] I've moved cities for someone
- [ ] I've dated soomeone I met on a dating app
- [ ] I've had an "almost relationship"
- [ ] I've never loved someone
- [ ] I've stayed in a relationship after I knew it wasn't right
- [ ] I've been blindsided by a breakup
- [ ] I've been emotionally cheated on
- [ ] I've had a one night stand
- [ ] I've had/been a friend with benefits
- [ ] I've felt lost

Check all the things you're willing to do to finally get it right. I'm willing to:

- [ ] Be radically honest with the people I date
- [ ] Have awkward conversations
- [ ] Say no when I'd normally say yes
- [ ] Say yes when I'd normally say no
- [ ] Trust my intuition
- [ ] Make my own decisions
- [ ] Leave uncomfortable situations
- [ ] Leave situationships
- [ ] Respect my energy and time
- [ ] Act on the red flag I see
- [ ] No longer be blinded by physical attraction
- [ ] Stop playing games
- [ ] Stay single for as long as it takes
- [ ] Never settle

What is your resolve? Write down 5 things you will never settle for in a relationship.

Chapter 3

Ok, we have a bit of a running start.

You are single and haven't found your person yet, BUT you've proven to yourself that you have a resolve to never settle.

You're living and dating with open eyes and an eager heart, and you're proud of that.

But let's back up. Let's get vulnerable and on the same page and understand WHY your relationships haven't worked out just yet.

Why? Why? Why?

If my experience has taught me anything, it's that when your dating life is in shambles, you can't seem to get it right, and you're constantly disappointed, you're likely not dating from the right place.

Simply put, you don't know your "why?"

Why are you dating?

What is your "why?"

I'm sure you've heard that said before.

What is your "why" in life?

Any article, podcast, or video on the topic of self-development, purpose, or living a happy life in general, tends to center on the need to find your why.

Why are you alive? Why do you do what you do? Why are you passionate about what you're passionate about? What is your "why?"

Maybe you've given it some thought in regard to your career, creative outlets, or purpose in life.

That's great!

But I'm willing to bet you haven't thought about your "why" in regard to dating and relationships.

Why do you date? Why are you looking for a partner in the first place?

Seriously! Think about that.

Why do you date? Why are you looking for your person?

I don't blame you for not asking yourself this question.

You date because you're human. It's just what you do. You're supposed to date. You're supposed to be in a relationship. It's biological. Life isn't meant to be lived alone.

But if you've wanted cuddles but you've only received struggles, you need to carefully consider your why. You need to get clear on why you're dating in the first place.

You make better dating decisions when you date from your place of "why."

At its core, knowing your "why" is impactful in life, because it gets you out of the gray of dating and relationships.

The gray is where you're trying to find your person. You're going on dates, but you have no real purpose other than it's just what you're supposed to do. It's what everyone else is doing.

You feel pressure to do it.

And so, you date in the gray area. Maybe you're dating because you feel lonely. Maybe it's because everyone else has found their someone and you're feeling the pressure. Maybe you're bored.

Dating in the gray is defined by a lack of clear vision for why you're doing what you're doing.

Without a strong "why," you're on autopilot. You go on dates; you meet people; you might go on a second date or two; you're swiping on the apps; but if you're honest, you're just going through the motions.

You want to find the right person for you, but if you were to sit down and ask yourself WHY you want to find that person in the first place, you wouldn't have a great answer.

You might say something like:

"I want to have someone in my life!"

"I want to share my life with someone!"

"Life isn't meant to be spent alone."

"I want to start a family."

But that's not a real "why."

Those are reactions to being alone. Those are reactions to being bored.

Those are reactions to what you think you're supposed to be doing.

You don't want to be alone, and that pressure, or even guilt, starts to add up. So you end up dating in the gray, aimlessly trying to find someone who "feels right."

My friend! Those weak "whys" simply are not going to work anymore. They haven't been working, have they? Right?

It's time you become purposeful about WHY you date. It's time you get clear on why you're dating in the first place.

Without a clear "why," it's like you're wandering around your apartment in the dark, trying to find your phone. It's like you're getting a massage while wearing a Canada Goose jacket.

You can do it, but it's not effective. And you're going to waste a lot of energy when all you have to do is turn the light on or lose that jacket.

Clarity. Simplicity.

> Stop being lost in the wind - giving your energy to anyone and everyone, in the hopes of finding someone who "feels right."

It's time to stop giving away your energy because you're just going through the motions.

It's time to stop giving away your shine unnecessarily because you don't know why you're doing it in the first place.

It's time to become intentional about why you're dating!

What is your "why?"

I can't answer that for you, but I can help you find clarity for yourself.

I'll tell you my "why," and then we can work together to put a finger on yours.

My "why"...

I date to find someone who unequivocally makes me a better person.

That's it!

Knowing my why has, without a doubt, improved my dating life.

When I approach dating firmly rooted in my why, it no longer matters if someone is attractive enough for me, has a good enough social circle, is funny enough, etc.

My bottom line is... does she make me a better person?

That is my "why."

I date to find someone who makes ME better.

That is so important, and it's not as cliché as it might sound.

Let me ask you a question:

Do you want to grow into the most bad*ss version of yourself?

Do you want to do all the things you've dreamed of - to travel, work hard, take on new challenges, experience new places, step out of your comfort zone, and genuinely push yourself?

Of course you do!

BUT until you share your personal growth with the right person, I really don't think you're all the way there.

You're close, but not all the way.

I firmly believe the right person will make you a better person, and your "why" should be rooted in that realization.

The right person will not only compliment you, be easy to get along with, kind, loving and attractive, but most importantly, that person will push you to become more. That person will show you your full potential.

This realization has helped me define my "why," and I hope it gives you something to think about.

Your "why" has to be more than:

"I want to share my life with someone."

"I want someone to care for and someone to care for me."

"I want someone to grow old with and explore the world with."

Your why needs to be specific, and actually, kind of selfish.

It's about YOU!

What is your selfish "why?"

In dating and relationships, you need to be more selfish! THAT is where your "why" comes from.

Dating has to be about YOU to start. It has to!

Yes, once you find your person, you need to drop a lot of that selfishness and deprioritize aspects of yourself and your life, but until you find that person, you need to be selfish.

You need to let that selfish "why" lead you to someone who is going to make you a better person.

You need to be selfish, and you need to be patient, because that person is worth waiting for.

The longer you wait and the pickier you get, the clearer your vision becomes to you. The right person is out there, and when you find him or her it will be very clear to you that he or she makes you a better person and you to them.

Your "why" will lead you to that person.

That person is someone who believes in you completely but challenges you completely.

It's someone who builds you up but isn't afraid to criticize you.

It's someone who accepts who you are, while demanding more of you at the same time.

It's someone who is genuine and kind, but not afraid to stand up for him or herself.

When you find clarity, your mission becomes simpler... all because your "why" is guiding you.

You no longer sit around hoping your person stumbles into your life. You no longer hope your person bursts through your living room wall like the Kool Aid® man and checks all the boxes you have.

You step out and you date from a place of purpose.

When you do, things get so much simpler!

The first question you ask yourself becomes, "Does he/she make me a better person? Does he/she help me grow?"

If the answer is no, you know what to do. Toodaloo.

Always being able to turn to your "why" simplifies your dating life, and right now, that's exactly what you need.

You need to simplify your dating life.

There are tons of people who might be "right" for you in other regards... right attraction, right sense of humor, right upbringing, right job, etc. Those are great qualities to look for, and you could find someone who checks those boxes, and you could probably make that relationship work.

But at the end of the day, it's all about YOU. It's all about whether that person makes you a better person.

So, what is your "why?"

Is it like mine? Is it completely different? Is it more specific?

Is it to find someone who challenges your bullsh*t? Your ego?

Is it to find someone who drives you to communicate and be vulnerable?

Is it to find someone who challenges you and your ideas, who doesn't just accept what you say?

Is it to find someone who is real and honest and pushes you to be the same way?

You have to define your "why" for yourself.

> Know that your "why" is more than just finding someone you get along with, or finding someone you feel comfortable around, or finding someone who makes you laugh, etc. It's more than just listing out a checklist of things you look for in someone.

Your "why" has to be personal and it has to go as deep as possible.

So, what is your "why?"

What is your "why" that is worth waiting for?

Remember that the right person will bring you into your own.

That's worth waiting for, don't you think?

It makes all the bullsh*t of dating worth it. It makes all the terrible Tinder® and Bumble® dates worth it. It makes all your past relationships worth it.

Your "why" guides you. It gives you purpose and conviction in dating. It gives you patience.

So take some time to define your "why!"

Stop wondering. Stop hoping for the right person or for love to find you.

Know your "why", date from a place of purpose, and I promise you that you'll find a way to get there.

Write down 5 things that make dating enjoyable for you.

Write down 5 ways the right person will improve your life.

THIS IS THE MOMENT.

Write down your BIG why. Circle it.

Chapter 4

Now that you've spent some time clarifying your "why," let's talk about using your newfound clarity to take back your power.

Let's be real... you've probably given it away.

When it comes to dating and relationships, the biggest mistake we make that results in us getting hurt, disappointed, let down, confused, cheated on, etc. is we give away our power, without realizing it.

We give away our power.

If you've found yourself stuck on the dating merry go round, going on date after date, feeling let down by or disappointed in how you've been treated, frustrated by the number of times you've been ghosted, the number of times you've felt unsure about what you're doing, or where you're heading... it's time you take back your power.

So here's the secret:

To take your power back in dating and relationships, you have to stop relying on potential.

You have to stop being blinded by potential.

Potential. KEY WORD POTENTIALLL

It's where you get in a relationship or go out with someone who takes forever to get back to you.

It's where you get ghosted, but you go back to that person when he or she finally decides to hit you up.

It's where you jump on that "u up?" text.

It's where you end up becoming blind to how bad someone is for you, even though the red flags are waving in your face.

Sound familiar?

You do those things, and you allow yourself to get in those situations, because you're blinded by the potential you so desperately want to see in that person.

Don't get me wrong, it's not a bad thing to want to see potential in someone.

Potential is important! It's important to believe in growth - what might be and what two people can become together. That's a huge motivator. That's the power of love and connection. Don't become numb or cynical to that.

But you should be a bit more aware of the crazy things that a blinding focus on potential can do to you.

To take back your power and put your "why" to use, you have to empower yourself to detach from a belief in potential and instead look at that person for who they are today. Right now. In this moment - whether it's someone you just met, have gone out with 3 times, or have been dating for a year.

Who is that person TODAY?

Who might that person grow to be?

What might you two grow to become together?

Those are three separate considerations, and you need to treat them as such.

If you lump them all together, that's how you become blind to red flags. You let potential make you blind to that fact that you've given away your power without realizing it.

When you only look at potential, here's what happens.

You start saying things like:

"He went through a lot in his last relationship, so I'm trying to be patient. I'm just giving him time, and it's going to be great."

"He only texts me on the weekends because he's so busy during the week. But once things settle down, it's going to be great."

"She said that hurtful thing to me, but she didn't mean it. We were drinking... it won't happen again."

Sound familiar?

You turn a blind eye to what you deserve right now because you're so fixated on potential!

Potential can be an intoxicating thing, and we need to be aware of this. We need to take back our power.

Taking back your power starts by realizing that someone can be a good person and they can have a lot of qualities you look for in a partner. You can meet them at just the right time in your life. You can be thinking, "Finally! Someone who seems right for me." You can feel a spark when you think about your life together.

But at the end of the day, just because it feels right in the moment... it doesn't mean they are your person.

Just because you see potential doesn't mean you should stay attached, giving your power away.

Consider that person or that relationship or whatever is going on in your dating life RIGHT NOW:

If you were to stop being the first one to reach out, what would happen?

If you were to stop calling or texting or setting up dates, what would happen?

If you were to stop fighting for them for a moment, what would happen?

Simply put: if you were to stop putting in effort, what would happen?

If you were to stop believing in potential for a moment and see what's happening right now, what would happen?

If you were to get out of your head and stop thinking about what COULD BE and instead focus on WHAT IS for a minute, what would happen?

You take back your power when you realize that you should never find yourself fighting for a TOMORROW with someone who isn't right for you TODAY.

You should never find yourself in a relationship where the only thing you have guiding you is belief in tomorrow's potential.

Let potential guide you later in your relationship. Let it guide you after you've become confident this person has something to offer right now.

Right now.

Take a good, hard look at that person as he or she is today. Take a good, hard look at how he or she communicates with you today. Take a good, hard look at how he or she treats you today, how he or she makes you feel today, and how he or she lives, loves, laughs, and works today.

If nothing were to change about that person, is that enough for you? Does it align with your "why" TODAY?

No? Then that person might not be the person for you, and it's important that you take action on that realization now.

It's important you let your "why" guide you early and often.

Don't remain stuck in a cycle of thinking defined by asking yourself, "WILL he/she make me happy," instead of, "DOES he/she make me happy?"

WILL that person make you happy vs. DOES that person make you happy?

Take back your power by refusing to be blindsided by potential.

Look at who that person is right now instead of who they might become.

Use projections of a future together as the icing on the cake. Let that vision make you excited about what's to come, but right now consider what is. Consider that person in this moment.

If they weren't to change at all, is that enough for you?

Asking yourself this will save you a lot of time. It can be a sobering moment when you realize you've been blinded by potential, but it's a powerful choice to make.

You deserve more. And you deserve more right now - not just in the form of potential in the future.

You get what you deserve by deciding to no longer waste your time.

Stop wasting your time, by letting go.

If you're holding onto hope for potential, and you're allowing yourself to be walked over or treated as a second priority, then you're holding on to something and someone who isn't right for you.

Stop it! Stop it right now!! Stop being thirsty for potential!

Stop spending time and giving away your energy.

Give yourself permission to sober up! Stop hanging onto the potential of someone who is not right for you today.

See things for what they are right now. No beer goggles.

Sober up, my friend, and take your power back.

Take back your power and see things for what they are right now - not three years from now, with a white picket fence and kids. Not two months from now, once things settle down at work or he or she finally gets over their last relationship.

Right now.

If you don't see it, if you don't feel it, maybe it's time to consider hitting the road.

If someone isn't showing up for you or is making you feel insecure or not at all appreciated, that should trump any belief in potential.

You deserve more, now. Not tomorrow. Now! Knowing that - and most importantly, acting on that - is how you take back your power.

You take your power back when you affirm that you deserve someone who loves you or cares about you in the same way you do to them - not the potential of that reality.

You deserve someone who is honest and forthcoming, who isn't sketchy, here for you and then not, who doesn't ghost you, gaslight you, love-bomb you, bench you, roster you, or whatever relationship catchphrase is trendy right now.

You deserve someone who makes you feel right, appreciated, good in this moment AND makes you feel hopeful for the potential of what's to come.

Equal parts. Not the other way around. Not the cart before the horse.

When you wake up to that and you see someone for who they are, right now, instead of who they might be, that's when you wake up to what you truly deserve. That's how you take your power back

---

You're not missing out, you're not falling behind where you're supposed-to be in life right now, you're not being selfish, you're not needlessly throwing away a good thing.

You're doing what's right for you. You're doing what's right for your "why."

What are 5 non-negotiable qualities you look for in someone TODAY? What do those actually look like in someone TODAY (not tomorrow)? What does that person do and say TODAY?

What makes you want to go on a second date with someone?

What are 5 ways you want to grow with your partner? What does a future together look like?

Chapter 5

PUT IT DOWN, FLIP IT AND REVERSE IT

How many times have you heard the following?

"If you want to find your person, you have to focus on you first."

Focus on you.

That's what every piece of dating advice says - just focus on you and the right person will become obvious to you.

As much as I used to scoff at that advice, there is, 100%, something to it. But the phrase could use some wordsmithing.

It's not, "Focus on you and the right person will become obvious." It should be, "Stop looking for 'the one' and become the one yourself."

This is it.

Stop looking for the perfect person and become the perfect person yourself.

Yes, that's it.

We spend so much time and energy looking for the right person.

We say things like:

"I've gotta find the right person."

"She's gotta be this, that, and this."

"I can't find him. I'm tired of lame dating apps and dates that just suck."

"I'm over awkward texting."

"Where is the one? I neeeeed to find the perfect person."

Feel that?

That's the wrong attitude.

Instead of wanting to find the perfect person to date and have a relationship with, become that person yourself.

Become the kind of person you want to be with.

This does something powerful, and it's more than just a nice phrase to put up on a wall next to live, laugh, love.

In the wise words of Missy Elliot, it's time to, "Put your thing down, flip it and reverse it."

I don't know what she actually means by that, but it applies here. Flip your thinking.

People say, "Focus on yourself! Focus on becoming your best self. Love yourself. Work on yourself, and then go out there."

Yes, true. Please do those things!

If you really want to find the right person and know it in your heart, you need to become THAT person yourself.

You need to work on yourself in respect to becoming that datable, relationship-worthy person.

Simply put, you need to work on exemplifying the very things you're looking for in someone else.

If you're the kind of person to have a checklist or a list of attributes you want in a partner, you need to exemplify those very things yourself.

This is a step we so often skip!

Skip it no more!

This single time right now should be a mix.

It should be a mix of the selfish: I'm going to do me right now. I'm going to focus on myself right now.

... AND the selfless: I'm going to become the person I want to date.

I really believe the only way to find and ultimately be compatible with someone who has all those amazing traits you want is to work on those same traits yourself.

You need to become that person.

Let's say, for example, you are looking for a sense of adventurousness, curiosity, drive, motivation, communication, and kindness in "your person."

Well, you'd be a bit of a hypocrite if you didn't embody those things yourself, right? It'd be tough for you to find someone who embodies those things if you don't yourself, don't you think?

How would you even know what they look like? How would you recognize them?

Take that checklist of things you look for in a partner and flip the script.

Do YOU embody those things? Are YOU working on those things?

Are YOU working to become adventurous, curious, driven, motivated, communicative, and kind?

Sidebar: I get that relationships are a compromise and the whole "opposites attract" thing, but if you want to find "the one" and you have a certain image in mind of what that person looks like, it only holds to logic that you should have those traits yourself, or at least be working on them yourself, yes?

That's the difference between "becoming your best self" and "becoming the one."

To find the one, you have to become the one.

When you dedicate your single time to this, what you're doing is refocusing - less on finding the perfect person and more on becoming that person and embodying those attributes yourself.

We tend to skip this step. But it's crucial!

We tend to focus on searching for a certain person, but we're not even close to being that person ourselves.

You might say that you're "working on yourself." That's great! I salute you! But are you working on the RIGHT things?

Are you working on the same things you want in someone else?

Probably not.

Flip the script.

Heed the wise words of Missy Elliot. When you do, things change.

When you start focusing less on FINDING and more on BECOMING, you'll notice that the kind of people you always used to date but always ended up having issues with... well, they suddenly aren't on your radar anymore.

That habit of ignoring the warning signs because he/she's a solid 10? Poof gone.

That habit of saying, "I'm gonna keep talking to her, because why not? I have nothing else to do?" Poof gone.

Gone is the temptation to date the same people. Gone is the usual lack of communication.

Gone is self-doubt. Gone is need for approval. Gone is a need to hook up or go on a second or third date to prove that you're witty, charming, or marketable.

Poof gone. Just like that.

In its place is a sudden and noticeable attraction to, and sense of being drawn to, the right people.

You become drawn to the right person, because you are becoming that person. Like becomes like. Like attracts like.

When you realize this, and you work toward it, you'll feel at peace. There's no pressure, there's no desperation, there's less searching, and instead, there's more being drawn to the right people.

Put your thing down, flip it and reverse it, and you'll change for the better.

You'll get much better at handling uncertainty.

You'll become more self-sufficient.

You'll start respecting yourself so much more.

You'll grow to only be interested in dating the right person - someone who communicates and of course is interested in you. Someone for whom you don't have to change into another person to make them like you. Someone who mirrors the attributes you've been working on yourself.

When you both come together, you'll be two "ones" meeting... not two people looking for the "one."

Does that make sense?

Psychologist Wayne Dyer has a quote about this that I really like:

"A relationship based on love... is one in which each partner allows the other to be what he or she chooses, with no expectations and no demands.

It is a simple association of two people who love each other so much that each would never expect the other to be something that he or she wouldn't choose for him or herself. It is a union of independence, rather than dependence."

When you switch from looking to becoming, I'm confident you'll begin to only date and approach people who are more in line with what you really want and need.

You'll do this organically. It'll happen naturally. And you'll just gel with that person, because there are no expectations. There are no demands. You're two independent people who are working on becoming "the one" together. There's no need for approvals. Nada.

There's just more certainty.

If you want to find the one, you have to become that person first. You have to work toward becoming that person first. You have to prioritize becoming that person first.

Stay single for as long as you need to. There's no pressure! There's no rush.

Until your mindset becomes less of a desperate search and a rush to find the perfect person, and more of "I'm going to become that person so I know what he or she looks like and there's no doubt..." stay single!

Feel me?

If you're single and frustrated because you've been looking and looking and putting yourself out there, but nada... then flip the script and become that person.

If you're honest with yourself, that hasn't been your priority. Your priority has been to find that person. Your priority has been looking! Your priority has been checking lists and then being frustrated when the person you're interested in comes up short.

No?

Well, then no wonder you keep dating the wrong people.

Do something about it.

Put your thing down, flip it, and reverse it. Do that, and you'll shed a lot of the fat in your dating life. You'll start making better decisions, and you'll see the incredible value of your single time.

Ask yourself: are you frantically searching, desperate to find "the one?"

Or have you found a balance where you prioritize becoming the one, so that finding the one is the easy side of the equation?

It's time to find that balance.

Flip the script. Become the one.

Write down 10 things YOU offer your partner.

Last chapter you wrote down 5 non-negotiable qualities you're looking for in someone today. Rewrite those qualities below and check all the ones you embody or are working on yourself.

Are there any opposite qualities you want in a partner? Write down as many you can think of.

Chapter 6

KANYE ATTITUDE

DRAKE FEELINGS

Have you ever noticed how we think and talk about relationships?

I wish I were in a relationship... I don't want to be single anymore.

As much as we know not to, we often lose sight of the person in favor of "the relationship" or a simple desire to not be alone anymore.

We see the forest instead of the trees.

We need to look at the trees!

We need to stop looking for a "relationship" and refocus on the person.

As with a lot of things in life, we put the cart before the horse.

We're so focused on "being in a relationship" or "finding a relationship" that we lose sight of what makes a relationship work - the two people in it! We lose sight of the attributes of "the one!"

So, I let's take a chapter to really, really, really focus on that other person.

How can you simplify what you look for in your person? You can have a list a mile long, but what really matters on that list?

In my opinion, you should look for a person who has two specific qualities first, and then add other qualities later.

Drown out the noise, put your list aside for a moment, and first look for these two qualities in that person:

Kanye confidence and Drake feelings.

You should look for someone who has Kanye attitude and Drake feelings.

Stop looking for a relationship. Stop picturing a relationship.

Use this single time to commit to looking for a person who has attitude and feelings - and as we talked about in the last chapter - become someone who has attitude and feelings.

I'm all about simplifying life, and these are the two most important qualities to look for in someone. Attitude and feelings.

Why?

When you find someone you can genuinely say has those two qualities or the capacity for them, you'll never be too much for them, your standards will never be too high, you'll be treated right, and you'll be seen for what you have to offer.

I'm quite literal in what I mean with those two qualities.

Look for someone who has attitude and feelings.

Your north star when dating should be: does this person have attitude? And does this person have feelings?

Attitude.

Not AN attitude. Not, "I'm a bad bitch, look at my swag", kind of vibe.

Do they have conviction? Do they have something that leads them and guides them?

Do they have a sense of being? A drive? A motivation?

I don't think you should be dating someone you need to fix. I don't think you should ever look at someone and say, "I can fix you. Let's do this."

No! You deserve better than that.

That's not to say you need to date someone who has their sh*t completely together, who is successful, confident and has Kanye-like swag.

I'm simply saying that you should look for someone who wants to be better, who wants to do more and make an impact, who has the drive to answer unanswered questions, who is curious and energized and wants more, who, when they don't know the answer to something, they look it up!

Your person needs some attitude. They need conviction, drive, and a sense of more.

Otherwise, you're setting yourself up for failure down the line.

A long-term relationship comes with more challenges and ups and downs than you can count. If you're not with someone who has at least some fire in their heart - fire to discover more, do more and think bigger - you're really going to struggle to navigate those moments.

Having attitude means dating someone who is there for you when you need them. It means they follow through with their promises.

It means they never think you're asking for too much.

It means they talk the talk and they walk the walk. They're stubborn, to an extent, and they follow through. They don't leave you wondering - or themselves for that matter.

They know that actions speak louder than words. That is Kanye attitude.

It doesn't have to be some exaggerated thing. It just has to be an internal fire.

They have that attitude - that fire, that sense of value and energy that makes them stubborn in a good way.

Most importantly, just as they are driven to be more themselves, they encourage that in you.

They support your passions, your hobbies, and your career. They get it when you cancel plans last minute because you have a project you're working on. They understand your drive. They would never give you an ultimatum to pick one or the other.

So, what do you look for in someone that is a good indicator that they have this Kanye attitude?

It's someone who is stubborn in a good way.

When life is up and down, how do they react? Do they throw everything away and give up? Do they just throw their hands up in the air and give up?

What do they do when they don't get their way? Do they pout and run off, or do they stick around and work to get it?

Are they stubborn in a good way because they have a north star that is compassionate and alive?

Would they rather smile than frown, and do they find a reason to do that? Would they rather say can or can't?

But most of all... do they fight for themselves in what they do, who they are and what they represent?

If they do, then in my experience, they'll be willing to fight for you.

That is the right attitude and it REALLY matters.

Obviously, someone can have these things and still not be right for you, but in my experience, knowing that someone has this attitude is so important. You need it yourself, and you're going to need it in a long-term relationship.

You also need balance.

And that's where the homie Drake and his feelings come in.

"Pain makes you stronger. Fear makes you braver. Heartbreak makes you wiser."
- Drake

Feelings.

Quite literally, feelings. Emotions. Being vulnerable. Being honest.

That is the second thing to look for. And we all know this, right?

We all know that the best relationships are built on communication and sharing of how one quite literally feels, but we lose sight of this so often, because we have an "I can fix him/her" mentality or a mindset that says that vulnerability will come in due time.

And, yes, to a certain extent, of course it will, but when you're dating and deciding what to do early on, I say put this at the top of your list of what to look for.

Do they have this ability? Do they have the drive to do it?

Maybe not on the first date, but are they vulnerable enough to express their Drake feelings?

Is that person willing to admit they're wrong?

That's a huge one! Are they willing to admit they're wrong?

Are they willing to say how they're feeling?

Or do they make you second guess everything? Do they make you feel lonely? Do they make you question your worth?

Or not? Do you know exactly how they feel because they have no problem saying it? Do you know your worth because they tell you how worthy you are?

That is what I mean by "Drake feelings," and it's the perfect balance to Kanye attitude.

They go together and complement each other, and that's why I say to simplify relationships. Those are the two things you should look for - with a big emphasis on Drake feelings.

Drake feelings means you can ask that person to express what they're feeling or thinking, and it isn't a big deal. You don't have to wonder. You don't have to overthink what they're thinking or not saying because you know that they have the capacity to share. And they do share!

And you can meet each other in the middle and never leave each other wondering.

This can take a lot of different forms, but it means looking for someone who is capable of having a deep, emotional conversation.

It's looking for someone who is flirty, likes joking around and talking about superficial things, but is also capable and eager to go deeper. They can talk about things they don't understand, about things that have eluded them, times they were wrong and times they disappointed themselves or others.

That is the best sign that someone is worthy of you.

Seriously!

If someone can't go deeper than talking about their weekend, nights out and their job You need to seriously evaluate why you're considering being with them.

Yes, sometimes it's not immediately apparent, but if you're looking for this quality early on, you'll learn to spot it quickly.

Feelings.

And attitude.

Other things are of course important - sense of humor, height and appearance, etc. But looking for these two qualities first and what they look like in practice will seriously simplify your relationships.

Attitude and feelings.

Do they have conviction, but are they also vulnerable?

Do they have drive, but also a sense of compassion for themselves and others?

That is the balance that eludes us so often, because we either get ahead of ourselves and start thinking about the relationship before the person, or we get distracted with things that we need to move past. Well he's tall! Or he's so funny! Or she's a 10! Or she's so chill!

Yes, those are important. But bump those down your priority list.

1. Attitude.

2. Feelings.

And then fill in the blanks with what supporting qualities you want in a person.

When you approach dating this way, you'll be able to quickly see who's right and wrong for you.

And then you'll no longer waste your time and energy.

You'll never think your standards are too high.

You'll know that you deserve more than basic conversations, basic communication, basic drive.

That's right!

You deserve someone who doesn't leave you guessing.

You deserve someone who supports your growth in the same way they are driven to support their own.

You deserve someone who doesn't give mixed signals.

You deserve someone who doesn't dismiss your ideas, hobbies, or passions.

You're not looking for too much when you want those things.

The best, most powerful connections come when you combine drive and vulnerability. Growth and compassion. Trips around the world with a weekend on the couch. Work hard play hard.

That's the vibe, and it's the balance we should all be looking for.

Look for someone who is stubborn in wanting to be their best self, who has a north star of values and drive, and who respects it when they see the same in you; who supports you and your drive to also be your best self. It's someone who never dismisses that.

And look for someone who is all up in their feelings. Who doesn't close off. Who doesn't leave you wondering. Who can admit when they're wrong or confused.

Those two qualities are, in my opinion, the yin and yang of a person who is right for you.

What are 5 ways you want your partner to make you feel? Write down 5 adjectives.

What are 5 things your partner is willing to do for you? Write down 5 actions.

Make us coffee in the AM???? <3

Write down 10 qualities you look for in someone else but start with:

1. Attitude

2. Feelings

3.

4.

5.

6.

7.

8.

9.

10.

Chapter 7

YOUR "HO" PHASE

Let's talk about how to make the most of your single time.

You now have a strong understanding of your why. You know the biggest pitfall to look out for.

You're committed to becoming the one so you can find the one. You are prioritizing attitude and feelings in both yourself and someone else.

Now you need to figure out what you don't know.

You need to get out there and live this. You need to get out there and get perspective and experience first-hand. This is essential!

Otherwise you run the risk of becoming one of those people who expects "their person" to magically show up in life.

Don't be one of those people! Those people wait and wait and wait until one day they end up settling for the first person who shows them interest.

You deserve better than that.

So, it's time for your "ho phase."

The better word here is your "experience phase" but it's easier to say "ho phase." You know what I mean.

This is your dating around, meeting new people phase.

It's during this phase when you actually validate what you want in a partner. It's during this phase when you really come to know what red flags to look out for. It's during this phase when you learn to trust yourself and you make quick, healthy, and compassionate decisions for yourself.

This phase is an opportunity.

It's an opportunity to come into your own, own your sh*t, discover more about yourself, and learn exactly what you want.

Finding "your person" requires a lot of trial and error, so you need to really put yourself out there. Pun not intended. :)

You discover this through experience. You discover this, and you solidify this, through your ho phase!

I considered not writing this chapter, because it's a pretty "duh" idea, but I've learned that we under-emphasize the importance of experience in dating.

We tend to assume that we can "think" ourselves into finding our person.

We assume that we can think ourselves into knowing the red flags to watch out for, our worth, and our compatibility. We assume we can find our person passively.

But my friend, that simply is not true!

You have to get out there and experience dating firsthand. There's no way around this.

Yeah, it might suck because you're sooooo over sh*tty dates. But the key to never going on another sh*tty date is going on one last one.

So put your pants on and let's go.

Your ho phase is essential to truly understanding what it is you want out of a partner... not what you think you want or what you've been told you want.

I'm talking about what YOU actually want.

What do YOU want in a partner?

... not what you think you want in a partner!

What do YOU want in a partner?

You've written your list of what you want in a partner, but why do you say those things? Is that YOUR list or what you think belongs on your list?

Now is the time to know with certainty.

Only you can discover this. You have to see it, feel it, touch it (uhhh), taste it (errrr) for yourself. No article, podcast or movie is going to make that decision for you.

Here's how I look at it: You can't meet someone in Hawaii when you're walking around the Los Angeles airport.

You can't find someone on a trip you refuse to go on.

Your ho phase is all about going on that trip for yourself and your single time is the time to do it. It's time to pack your bags and go on that trip.

Your single time is not a time to be sad that you're single, a time to be hung up on your last bad relationship, or a time to wallow in the fact that you feel lonely and that you're falling behind.

It's time to put your pants on and go!

It's time to celebrate the fact that you have an opportunity to get to know yourself better with the intention of finding someone who is right for you. And to do so at your own pace.

Simply put, I'm encouraging you to go on more dates, meet more people, introduce yourself more often and to just put yourself out there.

If that means firing up those dating apps you swore off, so be it.

If that means letting your friends set you up on a blind date, do it.

If that means giving out your number at a bar or asking for someone's, do it.

If that means sliding in the DM, do it.

Do whatever it takes to get more experience. Do whatever it takes to learn for yourself.

If that's not what you wanted to hear from me and you were hoping for me to give you some magic formula to finding "your person" without going on any more dates, I'm sorry to disappoint.

But I get it! I really do.

I know you might be over it! Soooooo over it. You're over the games, over the lack of commitment, over the apps. Everything.

But please see your single time for what it is. It is an opportunity.

Yes, it certainly is an opportunity to take pause, to find yourself, protect your energy and find your resolve.

But once it's time to rock... well, it's time to rock.

This is an opportunity to stop buying into other peoples' opinions, dating and relationship advice articles, what Cosmo says, etc. Heck... even what I say!

This is your chance to decide for yourself.

Everyone's experiences are unique, so let everyone else consider what works for them, and figure out for yourself what works for you.

Don't take all those articles you read too seriously. Don't take those memes seriously. Stop letting the Overheard in LA IG account lead you to assume something about dating.

Stop letting your friend - who honest to god is convinced that Aries and Virgos literally cannot date - influence you.

Don't listen to your friend who says you have to wait 3 days before calling or texting.

Don't listen to your friend who says you have to remain distant or act mysterious.

Figure that sh*t out for yourself!

Fact: you don't know what you don't know until you know it.

Seriously. You only learn through experience.

So, get out there and figure this out for yourself.

Rip the Band-Aid off and do it!

Don't buy into the hype or assume something until you experience it for yourself and can then make that decision with your own eyes and your own heart.

Stop buying into all the hype and red flags you've been told about.

Don't overthink things. Don't jump to conclusions. Find out for yourself.

Just because a dude posts banging selfies and bicep emojis doesn't mean he's a f***boy.

Just because a girl posts Marilyn Monroe quotes, loves Pretty Little Liars and a complicated Starbucks order doesn't she mean she's basic.

Figure those things out for yourself.

Don't dismiss someone immediately because you read somewhere that what they're doing is a red flag.

Your ho phase is a chance to learn to trust your intuition. This is an opportunity to trust your heart and see where it leads you.

It's better to follow your heart than to always follow your brain.

Big fan.

It's better to hurt or be hurt by someone as a result of following your heart than it is to waste your time or their time because you don't think things through for yourself.

Leaning into your heart saves time! It saves time, which in turn allows you to move onto the next experience so you can get closer to finding that one person.

Listen to your heart.

Fill your heart with experience and perspective!

One more time: You can't think yourself into knowing what and who is right or wrong for you.

Your ho phase is all about getting you out of your lukewarm state of mind.

Being lukewarm and liking everyone you go on a date with is lame!

It really is!

That means you don't have a strong sense of self. You can't possibly like everything in life... so how can you like everyone?

Just because someone is nice to you and is kind and courteous, does not mean they are "your person."

You'll learn this through experience.

Your ho phase is all about meeting new people, going on dates, and embracing this time as an opportunity.

You won't magically wake up and know what you want in a partner. You won't just wake up and know how to spot what you want in someone.

This workbook isn't going to give you that 100% clarity.

You have to learn how to spot it for yourself - what it looks like and what it means to you.

That comes from experience.

Recognizing the qualities you want in someone comes from spotting them in real life.

Mindset matters. Vibe matters. Personality matters. Kindness matters. Yes, being with someone who is good looking is fun.

But as John Mayer once said:

If you're pretty, you're pretty; but the only way to be beautiful is to be loving. Otherwise, it's just congratulations about your face.

It's true!

The more you embrace your ho phase, the quicker you'll come to realize this on your own.

You'll come to realize how important the other things in life are - and those are ultimately the things that make up "your person."

Your "ho" phase!

Focus on becoming "the one" and living your "why" and see dating and meeting other people as an opportunity to do that.

See it as an opportunity to build your self-respect and discover more about yourself.

Your ho phase is a point of growth, where you apologize for nothing and you say what you feel, and you mean what you say.

Doing this is a powerful thing.

When you combine resolve with an enthusiasm for experiences and thick skin, I'm confident you'll come to attract the right people in your life, and you'll be able to quickly weed out those who aren't right for you.

How do you envision meeting someone? Where? How? Write down 5 ways in the past you've met potential partners and 5 ways you would like to meet someone in the future.

Write down 5 characteristics of people you've dated in the past. Are there any patterns?

What are 5 physical characteristics you look for in someone? Did you include those last chapter in your list of 10?

Dimples tho.

Chapter 8

LOOKING IS FOR FREE

Let's get into the reality of dating. Let's get into the reality of your ho phase.

I like analogies, so here's how I look at things.

In life and dating, looking is free. Sampling the buffet is free. Window shopping is free.

A first date is free. A conversation on a dating app is free. A flirtatious DM is free.

But anything more from there is going to cost you. It's going to cost you your valuable energy.

Once you decide to go from sampling the menu to something more, it's going to cost you.

It's going to cost you your energy, if you decide to move forward while not acting on the red flags you saw in the beginning... while you're sampling.

If you decide to ignore those red flags because you like the attention that person is giving you, because you just don't want to be alone, or because that person is a 10, then it's going to cost you.

That's expensive! Your energy is costly! Your energy is valuable!

It's expensive, because the very signs you decide to ignore in the beginning are going to be exactly what causes things to go bad down the line.

The signs you ignore in the beginning just end up being the reasons you leave later.

And so, I say that with your "why" guiding you, you need to stop ignoring your gut reactions and your intuition.

You need to stop ignoring those signs in the beginning. You need to be confident enough and have more respect for yourself, so when your intuition tells you something, you act on it.

I've come to realize that even though we're all human, and sometimes it's fun to overlook certain red flags in favor of, uhhh, other attributes, it is an absolute bonehead move.

It's a bonehead move to see a red flag and yet decide to still give your energy away to someone who you know isn't right for you.

We all do this!

We all choose to ignore the signs for several reasons.

You don't want to be single anymore.

Everyone else has someone.

You're lonely... just you and your gravity blanket.

You're just so enthralled by the idea that someone else likes you, compliments you and gives you attention.

And so, you ignore the signs that are literally shouting in your face: this isn't a good idea!

We're all doing ourselves a huge disservice by ignoring those signs. Because, sure as the day is long, they'll come back to bite you, and when they do, you'll finally open your eyes and you'll say, "Yep... I knew this was gonna happen."

Don't ignore these!!!!!!!

Red flags.

You know that they will rob you of your energy and ultimately come back to bite you if you continue to ignore them.

So! Let's use this time together to make a commitment to act on those red flags.

Make a commitment to yourself to sample, sample, sample, but when you see a red flag, you move on.

It's that simple.

Draw a line in the sand and declare that you will no longer give your energy away to people who don't align with what you want.

It's nothing disrespectful. It's simply having respect for yourself and a sense of urgency about protecting your energy.

It might mean confrontation. It might mean an awkward conversation.

Regardless of how we respond to them, we need to stop bullsh*tting ourselves.

We need to be vulnerable enough to back away from people who we know aren't right for us - no matter how hot they are, no matter how much attention they give us, no matter how many followers they have on Instagram, no matter how good of friends they are with our family, no matter our past with them.

Why continue to give your energy to someone if you know those signs are going to be your downfall?

Sure, there's something to be said for working through problems, working together and compromising. I'm all for that. I'm not saying you should be like, welp, that's one sign - I'm out, and ignore the dozen other good signs that could outweigh any negatives.

I simply think we should all be more aware of the signs and make a commitment to not ignore them any longer. Keep an eye on them and promise to do what's best for us.

Have more respect for yourself and stop ignoring those things.

Don't go on that third date!

Don't commit to anything else!

Say no thanks and move on.

Do that, because it's the right thing for you, and because otherwise, you're wasting your time.

This is powerful, because it reminds you that you're in control of your dating life, and you get to decide who you date and who you give your energy, kindness, compassion, and heart to.

Acting on those red flags is a seriously empowering move.

When you do, you'll no longer feel the need to explain yourself. You'll become more confident in yourself. You'll stop settling. You'll become selfish, in a healthy way.

You stop putting yourself in situations where you're the side piece. You stop going on dates just to hook up. You stop trying to meet people at the club. You stop having ulterior motives or hidden agendas. You stop agreeing to 3rd, 4th, or 5th dates, knowing you have no intention of anything more.

You simply do what's right for you, because you've come to learn to no longer ignore the signs - the signs you've learned are indicative of people who just aren't right for you.

It's simple like that.

You know the red flags in your life. You've lived them, you've experienced them, and you've ignored them.

Red flags could be:

- trust issues
- someone obsessively focused on their dating checklist
- forceful about sex
- being passive aggressive
- never asking questions
- being selfish
- being rude to others
- being overly concerned with money
- someone who says something like, "If you can't handle me at my worst, you don't deserve me at my best."

Those are red flags. What are yours?

Remember that red flags don't necessarily make someone a bad person. It just means they're not right for you, because you value your time and energy.

You shouldn't feel like an *sshole or that you didn't give someone a chance!

In your dating life you might have previously said, "Give me a sign, universe! Is this person right for me?"

Maybe you grabbed your tarot card deck or consulted your horoscope.

Well, as you live your ho phase, you get signs. They're right there. You see them. You hear them. You feel them.

And at the end of the day, you can't ask for the signs and then ignore them.

Every time you acknowledge those signs and say no, you're doing yourself a huge favor.

No more. Raise the bar for yourself.

What are those red flags for you?

What are 5 things you ignored in previous relationships that caught up with you later?

What do you think are the 5 most important things that make a relationship work?

List out as many dating red flags as you can. Big ones or small ones.

Checked out the server XX

Chapter 9

SITUATIONSHIPS

Let's talk about something you'll inevitably run into during your ho phase.

Situationships.

Ya know... those ambiguous relationships? A relationship that isn't defined?

A situationship has no label and no commitment.

It's weird, murky... and frankly you deserve better.

You deserve better than to put yourself in a situationship, and you deserve better than to be situationshipped by someone else.

It's a huge compromise to your growth, and you should do everything in your power to not compromise yourself, your growth, and what you deserve.

You're more than capable of moving past ambiguous, no good, and vague relationships that aren't healthy for you.

Here's what I know:

If you're uncertain about what you want, you should be alone.

If the other person is uncertain about what THEY want, they should be alone (and so should you).

Either way you look at it, being unsure, means you shouldn't be in a relationship. You shouldn't be in a situationship.

If you're uncertain about what you want and you're in a situationship where you're hanging out with someone, hooking up and going on dates, but have no vision for your future - or you can't verbalize what the heck is going on - well my friend, it's safe to say that you don't know what you want.

If you can look yourself in the mirror and say, "I don't know what I want. I'm talking to this person, it seems serious on the surface, but there's zero sense of commitment or communication or future in my mind," that's a situationship. And you should say, "I need to get out of this."

If you're uncertain, you should be alone.

I don't think it's nearsighted.

Some people might react to this and say, "Case! You don't need commitment or clarity, early on in a relationship. Isn't that all a situationship is? It's that early stage of a relationship before it's DTR'd."

Yes, sure. Don't go all stage-5 on someone and be like WHAT ARE WE?! after 2 dates.

But there's a key distinction here.

What you're doing in a situationship is you're keeping your options open, and that other person is also keeping their options open.

You're keeping your options for someone who is better in some respect, and more importantly, you're keeping your options open for someone who you're sure about.

You're waiting around, killing time, having some fun, having a faux relationship, until you find someone you're sure about.

At its core, when you're in a situationship, you're unsure. You're unsure about that person and you're unsure about yourself.

That is a situationship and - rather crudely here - you should gtfo of it.

You can make that distinction, right?

It's not fair to the other person, but more importantly, it's not fair to yourself.

You're not doing any good for yourself.

When you're unsure of what you want, you should be alone.

Some people might say, "Well, Case, it's fine to be in a situationship, because being patient is part of discovering what you want in a relationship. What's the problem, dude?"

There's a difference between being patient and wasting your time.

There's a difference between being patient and quite literally holding yourself back

When you're in a situationship, you're not being honest with yourself or that other person. If you were sure, you'd want to shout from a mountain, "I really like you! We're great for each other! Let's DTR this thaaaang." Or, "Nah, this isn't right."

Or, at minimum, in your own head you could see a future together. You'd be excited about where it might lead. It's not just a warm body and company while you kill time.

At the end of the day, if you were sure, you wouldn't want to keep your options open.

I know that dating is not always that black and white. Like what the heck does it mean to be sure?

That's not an easy answer, I'll admit that.

But at a certain point in your life, you need to freakin' get real. You need to put on your adult pants and get sure.

So, in regard to situationships, I'd ask you:

When are you going to start listening to the real you?

The real you - that person who cares, is loving, kind, empathetic, open, and honest?

When are you going to listen to that person instead of allowing your primal, "keep my options open" mindset to run your dating life?

I say you deserve more than a situationship.

You deserve more than being with someone who is unsure, and you're better than being unsure yourself.

You deserve to listen to yourself and say, "I don't know what I want. I'm just doing this for fun, while I keep my options open."

It's empowering to admit that, and then make a decision to respect yourself and move on.

Because you deserve to be with someone you're sure about, whose name you want to shout from the mountain. You deserve to be with someone who, when you think about them, you feel warm and confident that you're doing the right thing, that there truly is a future there and you feel fine voicing that.

A situationship puts your life on hold!

When you're in a situationship, you're turning a blind eye to potential other partners.

You get sucked into a situationship. Even when you have no intention and you're like, "It's not serious. My options are waaaay open. It's just for fun," you get sucked in.

It's a time suck. You, like, black out and wake up 6 months later, and you're like, "Where am I? What the heck happened?"

Even though you say you're keeping your options open, in my experience, you turn your dating radar off and you put your life on hold.

You're with that person but not with that person. It's gray.

You're committed but clearly not, and in that time - however long you allow it to go on - you're turning a blind eye to the potential that is out there.

So again, I say... if you find yourself in a situationship where you're unsure, and you can sit down and have an honest conversation with yourself and be like, "Ya know what? I am unsure. I'm just keeping my options open." Then it's time to move on. Own that. Truly keep your options open, by moving on.

It's time to be real with yourself and say:

"I know why I'm doing this right now. This situationship is comfortable, I get to go on dates, we get to hook up, enjoy each other's company. Heck, it's better than being alone. It's harmless."

No! Being alone is so much better than a situationship.

It really is.

A situationship doesn't grow you. It doesn't provide any clarity. It confuses you. It doesn't move you any closer to living your "why" or becoming the one yourself, like we've talked about.

At the end of the day, dating is trial and error. The purpose of dating is to meet someone, get to know them at a decent level, and then ask yourself, "Do I want to keep moving forward? Yes? Ok, let's do it. No? Ok, sayonara."

But in a situationship, you're making no decision at all!

You're settling. Plain and simple.

Don't try to rationalize it and say you're just being patient, kicking the tires, or figuring out what you actually want.

You figure that out by DOING, and in a situationship you're doing exactly nothing.

The very fact that you're in a situationship is proof enough that you're unsure. And if you're unsure, move on.

Dating - like, actually dating with intention - is about being authentic. It's about setting boundaries.

It's about being freakin' vulnerable.

If you want to find the right someone, just as you have to be sure of them, you have to be sure of yourself.

Keeping a roster, a backburner, being in a situationship... it means you are not sure of yourself.

Plain and simple. You don't know what you want.

But the good news is, you can learn what you want. And the first step to figuring that out is to get out of that situationship.

Being sure of yourself means you stop texting with that person, you stop sexting with that person, you delete that contact, you stop DMing and flirting for no good reason.

It means you stand your freakin' ground and say, "I want to be sure. I want to be sure of myself, so I can be sure of someone else."

That's what dating is about.

Sure, have some fun! Go nuts! Who am I to judge?

But when you decide to get serious, get serious.

Step one is getting yourself out of any and all situationships.

Stop making excuses! If you want a relationship, go find one. Stop letting your unsureness allow you to stay in that situationship.

Don't try to be that cool, laid back, chill person who's like, "It's whatever, no biggie."

Yes! It is whatever! It is a biggie! It's your life!

How are you going be unsure about something but keep doing it, and doing it, and doing it.

Stop not making a decision. If you're unsure, get sure. Do something to figure it out. If you're still unsure, then peace out.

It's that simple.

Keep moving. Don't settle for a situationship. You deserve more than that from someone else, and you should demand more respect from yourself.

No more allowing yourself to live in the ambiguous gray area of being unsure, yet doing nothing about it.

Don't allow your loneliness to cause you to stick out a situationship.

You deserve more.

You deserve to say, "Yes, I am sure!" And you deserve someone to say, "Yes, I am sure," about you as well.

Until that is the case or until you find someone who you want to become sure about, stay alone.

That's the real power move. Single is a freaking power move!

There's absolutely nothing wrong with that, and I hope you'll honor the power you have to make decisions that are best for you.

Honor the ability you have to be honest and sure with yourself, so you can be honest and sure about someone else.

What are 5 things you demand from yourself in a relationship? How do you respect yourself in a relationship?

What are 5 things you're sure of about yourself in life? This could be something about who you are, your values, your passions, etc.

If you're unsure about someone, how can you become sure? List out 5 ways you can figure it out.

Chapter 10

THE REAL LOVE LANGUAGE

Let's talk love languages for a moment.

Reread how I ended last chapter.

I said, "Honor the ability you have to be honest and sure with yourself so that you can be honest and sure about someone else."

Honest! Both with yourself and others!

THAT should be your love language.

Honesty should be your love language.

It should be what you look for in someone else, it should be something you push yourself to be, it should be how you express your love, and it should be something you're proud of being.

Radically honest.

No holds barred, no time wasted, just honest.

It should be something you pride yourself in being and you should know that you deserve someone who is the same way.

That should be your love language!

You should be honest, upfront, and real. And expect the same from someone else.

I know this can be a challenge. It can be awkward and embarrassing, and in dating, your career, or social interactions, it's not always applauded.

We're told not to act too interested in someone. We're told to pretend to not care or to pretend to be disinterested, because we don't want to seem "easy." We're told that playing hard to get is the way to be. We're told to sugarcoat feedback.

And so, we wind up going along with things we don't want to. We pretend to not care about certain things - our passions and the things that make us weird.

But we need to stop and instead adopt a mindset that is honest. It's a mindset that says:

If I like you, I'm going to tell you! I'm not going to play games with you, and I'm not going to play games with myself.

I'll laugh if it's funny. I'll cry if it's sad. I'll overreact if it means a lot to me.

If I'm passionate about something, I'll talk about it.

If I have a question, I'll ask it.

I'll say what's in my heart and ask the questions that are in my head.

That is radical honesty, and it goes a long, long, long way - particularly in your dating life.

Be rad.

We need to stop allowing this tendency we have, to not be honest with others, to exist in our lives any longer.

We don't do it maliciously. We're not intentionally trying to mislead. It's just something we've grown to do, and unfortunately, it's become a part of who we are.

We curate who we are with how we want to come off with the things we say, the way we dress, etc.

We hide our true intentions and feelings, because it's a defense mechanism.

You can't get hurt if you don't say what you really feel, right? You can't get hurt if you refuse to be sensitive or honest.

It's become easy for us to say, "Pshhhh I don't care. Nah, I'm not looking for anything serious. I don't care if I'm rejected."

The truth is, you do care. Of course you do! You do care!

But we don't want to be hurt, and so we dull our shine. We bite our tongue. We refuse to care, because if we did, and we admitted it, we run the chance of being turned down, rejected or embarrassed.

And so, we've grown to wear this like armor.

"Who me?! Nah, I don't really like her."

"Who me?! What, are you kidding? I love my job!"

"Who me? I love my friend group! Super great group of people."

I really think the path to a happy and fulfilling dating life is one where you strip yourself of this tendency to not be honest.

Simple. No fluff. Just honest.

Otherwise, you're missing out on genuine connection with others. When you settle for anything less than honesty with yourself, in what you say and do, you're missing out on the world around you, your partner, and yourself.

You miss out on depth, on feeling close and real. You miss out on real connection.

You miss out on living your truth and saying real, vulnerable, honest things like:

I'm struggling. I've messed up. I'm not always as happy as I seem. I don't have everything figured out. I'm weird and quirky. I'm passionate about xyz. I'm really interested in this.

Say those kinds of things! Shout those feelings and don't be afraid of how it might make you seem.

Be too much to handle. Be too loud, too passionate, too emotional, too sensitive.

That is radical honesty and that should be your love language, because it's real. And you need real to not only find your person but also to make a relationship work with them.

So, make that your love language and look for the same in the people you date.

You know you've found someone who is good for you when you no longer feel the need to hide certain things - when you feel energized to be honest with that person and honest with yourself, and it becomes this great fulfilling cycle of honesty. That's the real love language.

I don't think you need to wait until you've found someone, and you're months in, finally feeling the vulnerability, and you know you have to be honest.

Why wait?

Why not live your life in the fast lane?! Why not live your life with 24/7 radical honesty?

It seriously sets you free and attracts the same kind of people into your life.

I'm not talking about first date "I have issues" type talk. That's a bit much.

I'm simply talking about being honest as a starting point for who you are, how you date, and what you look for in someone else.

Have real conversations, real interactions and real moments with real feelings and real honesty.It's not a way to unload your insecurities or issues onto someone else. It's simply a practice of radical candor. It's a practice of honesty that exudes from you in everything you do. You simply hide nothing.

When honesty is your love language, you don't want to hide anything from yourself, and in turn, you don't want to hide anything from those around you.

You proclaim your passions. You ask your questions. You clarify intent.

When you practice radical honesty yourself, you begin to look for that same willingness and vulnerability in everyone else. And, whether or not this is your real love language, (personally I'm a words of affirmation/ physical touch kinda guy), it's going to seriously simplify your dating life.

Say, "I messed up," instead of making an excuse.

Be honest and don't try to come across as perfect.

Use that as the way you express your love for yourself and your love for someone else.

It means letting your real self shine through. It means listening to your soul and no longer keeping what it says beneath the surface.

It means not waiting around for someone to come along and drag your real feelings out of you.

You do it yourself, and you own it, because that's not only the truest form of self-love but it will lead you to someone who is right for you - who respects that and who reciprocates it himself/herself.

That is how you deserve to live, and that is how you deserve to love and be loved.

Relax. Drop that armor. Drop that filter, and loosen your grip a bit.

It's a serious power move, and like attracts like, right? So, stand for honesty and attract someone who practices it themselves.

In previous relationships, what are 3 things you never told your partner?

Write down 5 things you refuse to fake in life.

Be honest... what do you want right now? What is your gut reaction to this question?

Chapter 11

YOU'RE MORE THAN JUST A SNACK

Let's talk about YOU.

You know your why.

You know the red flags to look out for.

You know what big thing might distract you or blind you (not that big thing lol).

You know what you want in someone, and you know that you need to work on those same things yourself.

But there's still one other piece of the puzzle that we need to address.

We need to break down one last barrier. And that's a barrier defined by the things you're still faking. The filter you still put on and the disguises you continue to wear.

Simply put, you're not going to find a fulfilling relationship while you're faking anything (mmmmk?).

We just talked about radical honesty, and in Chapter 6, we talked about the idea that like attracts likes. So, if you're faking who you are, adjusting who you are around other people, or living a dual life, you're going to attract that same kind of person.

And that's not what you want, right? You deserve more than that, right? If you're not honest with yourself or the people around you, you're going to attract that same kind of person.

The fact of the matter is, dating requires radical honesty - with yourself and with others. That's your love language now, right?

So, if you're faking things left and right in your life, if you're not being your true self - how do you expect to know who is right for you and who is not?

Let's back up a bit and talk broadly about YOU.

To find your person and enjoy dating while you do, you have to live your truth.

Live your truth.

Have you heard that before? What does that even mean?

That's a lower back tattoo if I've ever seen one.

What if you don't know what your truth is?

TBH I don't really know, but I do know that it's easier to know what your truth is not.

So, let's start there.

It's easy to know when you're faking something.

It's easy to know when you're forcing something.

And when you're doing that, you're not living your truth.

And that's no bueno.

So! It's time to stop forcing things in your life.

And the best place to start is to stop forcing yourself to be a "snack."

Being a snack! That's going to be the analogy here. :)

You're more than just a snack. You are the whole freakin meal.

Everyone likes a snack! A snack is tasty. A snack is a snack.

Being a snack is cool, I suppose. A snack dresses cool, talks cool, does cool sh*t. In the moment, a snack is loved by everyone.

It's easy to be a snack. You say the right things, dress the right way, hang out with the right people, post the right things on Instagram, have the right hobbies, watch the right movies or sports.

You talk the snack talk and walk the snack walk.

But if you go your entire life trying to be a snack - being loved by everyone - you're going to end up faking a lot of things. You're going to end up forcing yourself to be someone you're not.

I say screw that!

Be the whole meal. Stop faking things in your life. Stop forcing yourself to be someone you're not, to hang out with people who are not right for you, to say things, do things, be a person that is not real to you.

Be fine with not being liked! It's ok!

The reality of life is that we all lead ourselves to move further from our truths. We all do this. BIG time.

We fake happiness. We fake that we're into things we're not. We force relationships, we force hobbies, and we force mindsets. We force ourselves into a version that is not real to us.

But at the end of the day, you can't force yourself to be someone you're not.

Eventually it's going to catch up to you, and you're going to realize that you wasted a lot of time, energy and empathy playing that game.

The reality is that, as a human, you were not designed to be liked by everyone.

You were not designed to be liked by everyone.

I'm going to sound like a broken record with how many times I probably say this but here it is again:

You were not designed to be liked by everyone.

You don't need to be liked by everyone else!

You have more to offer than being a snack!

The more you fake it, the further you get from your "why" and the further you get from becoming "the one."

The most helpful thing I can tell you is that when it comes to dating, you were not designed to be liked by everyone.

If you make it your mission to be that way, you're inevitably and passively moving away from your truth. Oh, and dating is going to really suck for you, because you're going to massively overthink things

You're more than just a snack.

A snack gets nods of approval and praise. But the whole meal is more complex than that. Not everyone loves the whole meal.

And I implore you to be the whole meal!

Be your entire true self.

Even if you don't know what your truth is yet, push yourself to be your whole entire self - true to how you feel and who you are.

That might be someone who is not loved and applauded by everyone. That's ok!

You know the feeling of when you're forcing something. You know when you're forcing yourself to be someone you're not because you want to be a snack.

We all do this. We all force ourselves to do certain things, so we're accepted.

As good as it feels in the moment, at a certain point you're going to realize that it's not helping you grow. It certainly isn't helping you find "your person." It's a distraction and a waste of your energy.

Be the whole meal.

You were not designed to be liked by everyone!

One more time for the people in the back:

You were not designed for everyone to like you!

This is such a powerful thing for you to realize.

Be yourself! Again, it's not always clear who you are - you can spend an entire lifetime figuring that out - but deep down you know who you are not. You know when you're forcing yourself to do, think, and say things that aren't true to you.

Know that being a snack is fun for a bit, but it doesn't grow you. It doesn't evolve you. It doesn't make you happy. It's fleeting.

If you're not the chill girl, don't pretend to be!

If you're not into casual sex, don't pretend to be!

If you'd rather paint than go out day drinking, own that!

Right?

You're more than just a snack. You have truth, values, and passions that are yours and yours alone. You should honor them. You should honor the fact that you were not designed for everyone to like you!

You cannot force yourself to be someone you're not.

You cannot force yourself to believe in things that are not real to you.

You cannot force yourself to be a certain way, to say the right things, dress a certain way or hang out with certain people that are not real to you.

You can for a bit, but you know it's forced when you do. And forced time is wasted time.

So, when it comes to your dating life, if you're finding yourself being a snack, take pause and remind yourself to be the whole meal.

Otherwise you're wasting your time.

Time is your life's most important asset. And you should honor that.

You should spend less time trying to be a snack and more time being the whole meal.

Spend less time adapting to people and circumstances, less time allowing people who aren't meant for you to be part of your life, and less time trying to make everyone happy, even when it makes you miserable or unfulfilled.

That's less time living for others and more time being true to yourself in some form - whatever that may be.

It might be simply rethinking your friendships or what you do with your free time.

It might be finally standing up and being your true weird self.

It might be finally embracing that passion or that hobby of yours - that hobby you used to hide because you didn't look like a snack doing it.

It might be making that joke that really is who you are, but you don't usually because it might not be appreciated by everyone else.

It might be giving feedback to someone or multiple people - feedback that you've kept quiet before, because it's honest and potentially hard to hear.

You were not designed for everyone to like you!

Know that it's OK to not be loved by everyone. It's OK if not everyone is drawn to you, or supports you, or claps for you. It's OK if someone doesn't understand your sense of humor.

It's OK if someone thinks you're too loud or too quiet. It's OK if someone thinks you're weird or eccentric. It's OK!

It's OK if not everyone thinks you're a snack.

What matters is that you're the whole meal - to yourself.

What matters is that you push yourself to not force things anymore.

Great things happen when you stop forcing things.

You'll be drawn to the right people and the right people will be drawn to you.

You'll start doing more of the things that YOU want to do, without caring what other people will think, without hoping it's accepted.

You'll start speaking your truth - whether that's a bad joke, an observation, or a deep question about life and sunsets.

Simply put, you'll stop forcing things, because you embrace the fact that you don't need everyone to think you're a snack.

Sure, be a snack on a Friday night out - that's fun. Have at it, you little snack you!

But push yourself to be the whole meal to yourself - so that when you look around at your relationships, your dating life, what you do, what you say, how you dress, how you carry yourself... you know you're not forcing anything.

Sometimes, getting to this point requires drastic change. It might require a couple "bye, Felicias" or some big mindset and habit shifts, but have the confidence to know that embracing this is going to lead you in the right direction in your dating life.

It's going to make rejection OK. It's going to give you the confidence to stay in your lane. It's going to make you feel at peace when someone's not into you. It's going to lead you to find peace and not overthink every "what if."

Always trying to be liked, adored, or accepted essentially leads you in circles. And that leads you nowhere. It's a constant cycle of approval.

Say, "Enough!" Stop forcing yourself to be someone you're not. Break free of that cycle.

When you're no longer going in circles, you're free to head in new and exciting directions, to meet new and exciting people, to discover new and exciting things about yourself, and to find out what offers you true happiness and fulfillment. That is never wasted time.

BYE FELICIA.......

What are 5 words someone would use to describe you?

Write down 5 adjectives that DO NOT describe you. Write down 5 things you DON'T like to do.

What are 5 things you love about yourself?

I'm too fun.

Chapter 12

SINGLE IS YOUR SUPER POWER

So, that's it, my friend!

I hope this short workbook has empowered you to take a step back from what you've been doing, what you've been thinking, and the story you've been telling yourself.

I hope you now have a bit more clarity - even if it's only a little more.

I can't wait to see what you do with it. :)

Use your clarity to have more patience, know your worth, and see dating for what it is - an opportunity to live your truth.

Your truth is living in a way that reflects your why, the worth you see in yourself, the confidence you're building, and the vulnerability you show as you go about dating.

I hope you tell yourself a different story now.

I hope you've turned your back on stories like:

"Dating sucks and is filled with dishonest, non-committal people."

"No one gets me! I don't think there's a person out there for me."

"I'll never get over what's happened in my dating life."

Instead of those stories, I hope you're now telling yourself a more uplifting story - a story that says you've lived and learned, and you're better for it, because you refuse to settle.

Whether you're screaming this new story from a mountain or just nodding your head right now, you're living this story.

There's no better sign of this than the very fact that you're single right now. You read and completed this workbook because you want to do better and you still refuse to settle.

That's proof enough!

I hope you're approaching your dating life now with a new vigor, balanced with patience.

I hope you're telling yourself a story that makes you smile because you know it will all be worth it.

It will all be worth it!

All the sh*tty dates, the frustrating relationships, the situationships... it will all be worth it!

It will all be worth it, because you have taken the time to know who you are, what you want, and why you date.

You have more faith in yourself now than you did before you started this workbook. You know that you're capable and worthy of finding what you deserve.

You know you have what it takes to make better decisions. You know when to check yourself.

You know how to stop assuming and to stop being blinded by potential. You have a newfound respect for yourself.

So, ride this momentum. Feel energized with this workbook and make it last.

See it in yourself, with everything that happens in your dating life.

Most of all, know that love is always worth the try. Being vulnerable and being hurt or rejected is always worth the shot.

Promise yourself that you will be the open, soft, vulnerable person you're capable of being.

Don't let your past dating frustrations make you cold or closed off.

Open yourself up and watch how the world opens up to you!

I said it several times throughout this workbook: like attracts like. Be soft, open and honest. Tell the universe what you want instead of what you don't want.

Think that's overly cheesy?

OK, but just give it a try. Give it a shot for the next 6 months. Do the opposite of what you've been doing for the next 6 months.

Spend the next 6 months with all you've learned about yourself in this workbook and channel it to be your most vulnerable but centered self.

Don't take no sh*t, but be vulnerable!

Say yes when you want to. Say no when you want to.

Don't be afraid to do a complete 180 from how you used to be. Throw out the rulebook that your parents gave you. Throw out the rulebook that you read in some magazine or heard on some podcast.

Create your own set of rules, based on why you date and the person you want to be.

Forget what you've been told about how you're supposed to act, what you're supposed to say or what you're supposed to feel.

Make your own rules!

You have it in you to act on the realizations you've come to in this workbook.

At the end of the day, you were put on this earth to live your truth. You were put on this earth to let people in, to be soft and to feel.

You were put on this earth to love yourself and to share that love with someone else. Don't rush it, my friend!

You are worthy. So incredibly worthy!

So, use this single time to affirm that.

Single is your superpower!

Your superpower is knowing that you will never settle.

Your superpower is knowing "why" you're dating.

Your superpower is opening your eyes to what is, instead of what might be.

Your superpower is finding out for yourself what you want - not what you think you want.

Your superpower is listening to your intuition and respecting what you know deep down to be true.

Your superpower is establishing boundaries and acting on them.

Your superpower is being OK with not being loved by everyone. It's celebrating that!

Your superpower is living all those truths and being excited as you do.

Your superpower is taking every bad date or frustrating relationship issue and never allowing it to put a damper on your open eyes and eager heart.

Open eyes and an eager heart!

That means knowing yourself, knowing what you deserve, and never looking back.

THAT is your superpower, and I hope you proclaim it during this time of being single.

What is your why?

I am committed to: (check as many as you want)

- [ ] Listening to my intuition
- [ ] No longer ignoring red flags
- [ ] Recognizing my worth
- [ ] Becoming the one
- [ ] Being stubborn about what's right for me
- [ ] Staying single if I'm unsure
- [ ] Being grateful for the lesson I learn
- [ ] Focusing on today rather than tomorrow
- [ ] Looking for attitude and feelings
- [ ] Being radically honest with myself
- [ ] Being radically honest with those I date

Trace these letters.

I WILL

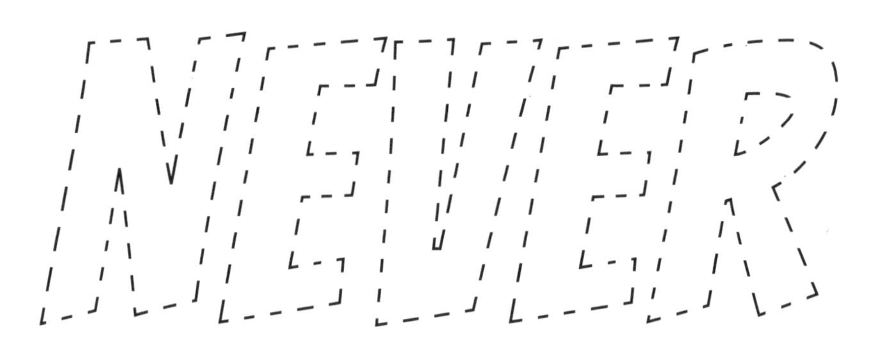

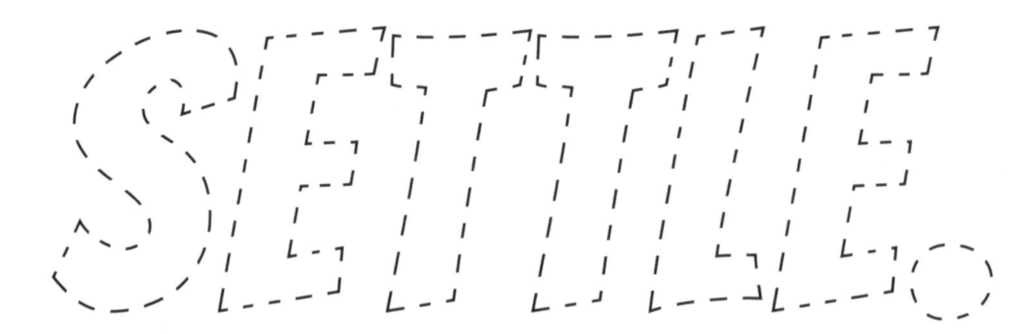

That's it!

Let's hang out on Instagram. **@case.kenny**

Want more?

Check out **newmindsetwhodis.com.**